This book belongs to

_____

Now That You Are Five

Written by Matthew Ralph

Now that you are five, so many amazing things have happened in the world.

Let's find out some of them together!

Now that you are five, 1,825 days

have passed.

In that time, you could sail around the world

46 times at the fastest speed.

Now that you are five, you've slept for around

21,900 hours.

That is the equivalent of 913 days!

Now that you are five, you have eaten

at least 5,475 times.

Which food do you like the most?

Now that you are five, your brain has at least doubled in size since you were born.

That is why you are such a smart cookie!

Now that you are five, you have drunk at least

14,600 glasses of water/fluid.

That is the same as 12.1 bathtubs!

Now that you are five, the moon has orbited around the Earth 65 times.

And it travels at a speed of 2,288 miles per hour. That's enough to make anyone feel dizzy!

Now that you are five, Mount Everest has grown

by 1 inch.

Are you growing faster than that?

Now that you are five, an albatross has flown continuously, only touching the ground five times. That's a lot of flapping!

How many times can you flap your arms in a minute?

Now that you are five, you have smiled at least

130,000 times.

Show us your best smile!

And even though so many things have happened

since you turned five,

one thing will always continue to grow...

How much I love you,

and always will!

Join in the fun!

Get creative

Spot the 10 differences

Word Search

```
V  S  X  W  Y  X  E  Q  P  P
I  E  L  Q  A  S  B  D  C  X
P  P  R  E  G  C  A  L  G  I
E  V  E  R  E  S  T  A  E  Y
N  C  Q  Z  K  P  H  U  U  E
F  B  Y  Z  Q  G  T  G  R  M
A  E  N  S  K  S  U  H  K  R
Q  M  O  O  N  N  B  J  D  H
J  C  S  M  I  L  E  S  D  C
N  C  V  L  O  V  E  L  H  T
```

Age   Sleep   Laugh   Everest

Smile   Moon   Bathtub   Love

Answers

Did you manage to solve all of the activities?

Well, visit the website below to find out the answers.

But... you will need the SECRET PASSCODE in order to access the page. Do not tell anyone what it is though!

www.mattralphthewriter.com/answers

About the author

Matthew Ralph is a children's book author who lives in London, England.

When he is not busy writing his next book, he enjoys drinking tea, eating fish & chips and waving at The Queen.

Matthew always enjoys hearing from his lovely readers as well as reading your comments. If you liked this book, please leave a review!

If you would like to learn more about him, visit his website:

www.mattralphthewriter.com

Get a FREE sloth-themed Digital Activity Book based on Matthew's best-selling book "Sam The Speedy Sloth."

The activity book includes coloring pages, spot the difference, word searches and a fun rainforest quiz!

Sign up to Matthew's newsletter to get this FREE activity book as well as news, updates and exclusive discounts:

www.mattralphthewriter.com/sign-up

More books by Matthew Ralph

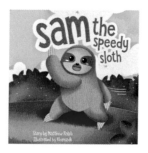

Sam The Speedy Sloth

The Adventures of Sam The
Speedy Sloth:
Playtime in the rainforest

Family Means…

Gia The Not Giant Giraffe

Personalized Sloth Book

Personalized Giraffe Book

Go On… Press It

Spot The Difference

ABC Animal Facts

www.mattralphthewriter.com